animorphia

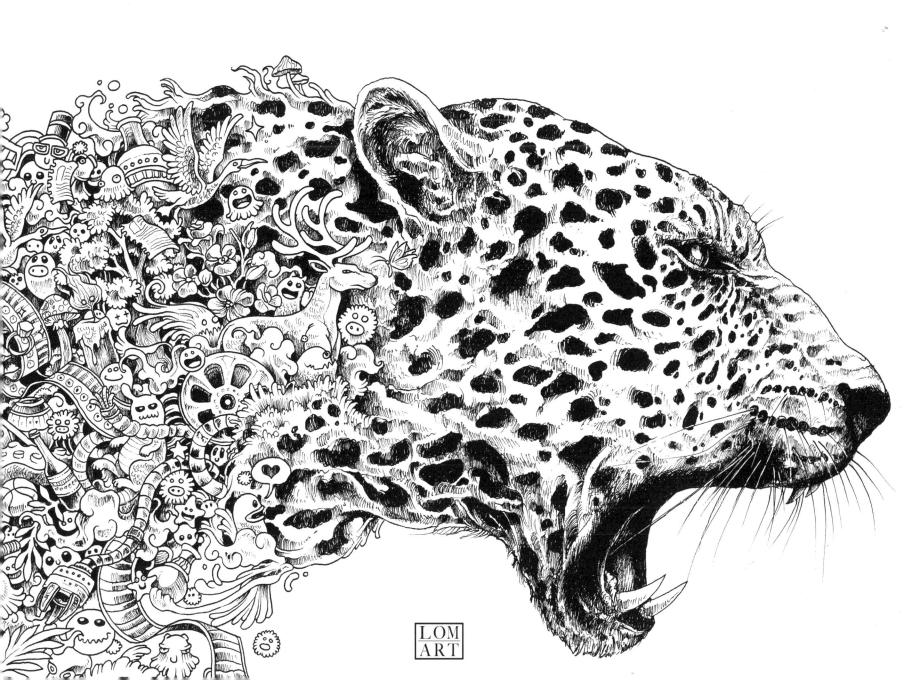

LOM ART

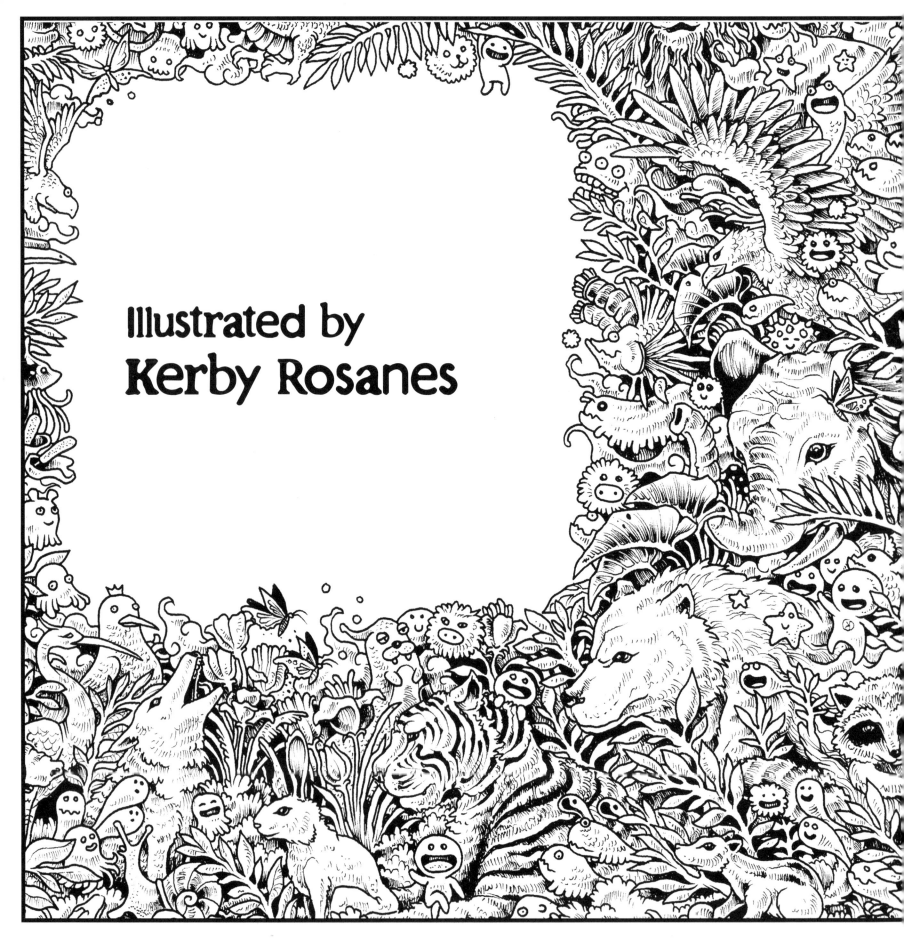

Illustrated by
Kerby Rosanes

This book belongs to

....

Edited by Jonny Marx
Designed by Zoe Bradley
Cover design by Angie Allison and John Bigwood

With thanks to Hannah Thornton
for being a great talent scout

First published in Great Britain in 2015 by
LOM ART, an imprint of Michael O'Mara Books Limited,
9 Lion Yard, Tremadoc Road, London SW4 7NQ

W   www.mombooks.com

f   Michael O'Mara Books

🐦   @OMaraBooks

A CIP catalogue record for this book is available from the British Library.

ISBN: 978-1-910552-07-0

7 9 10 8 6

This book was printed in Italy.

Welcome to this creative colouring adventure!

Delve into my high-definition, super-detailed doodle world, where strange creatures morph and meld into amazing animals and beguiling beasts.

Each detailed drawing has been crafted with fineliner pens and can be coloured in any way you like. There are also doodle pages that you can complete, customise and embellish in black line.

Keep your eyes peeled for unusual objects scattered throughout the pages. You'll find a list of hidden treasures that you need to search for at the back of the book (along with all of the answers).

Kerby Rosanes

Create more creatures riding the waves.

Fill the ram's horns with doodles.

Fill the butterflies
with detail.

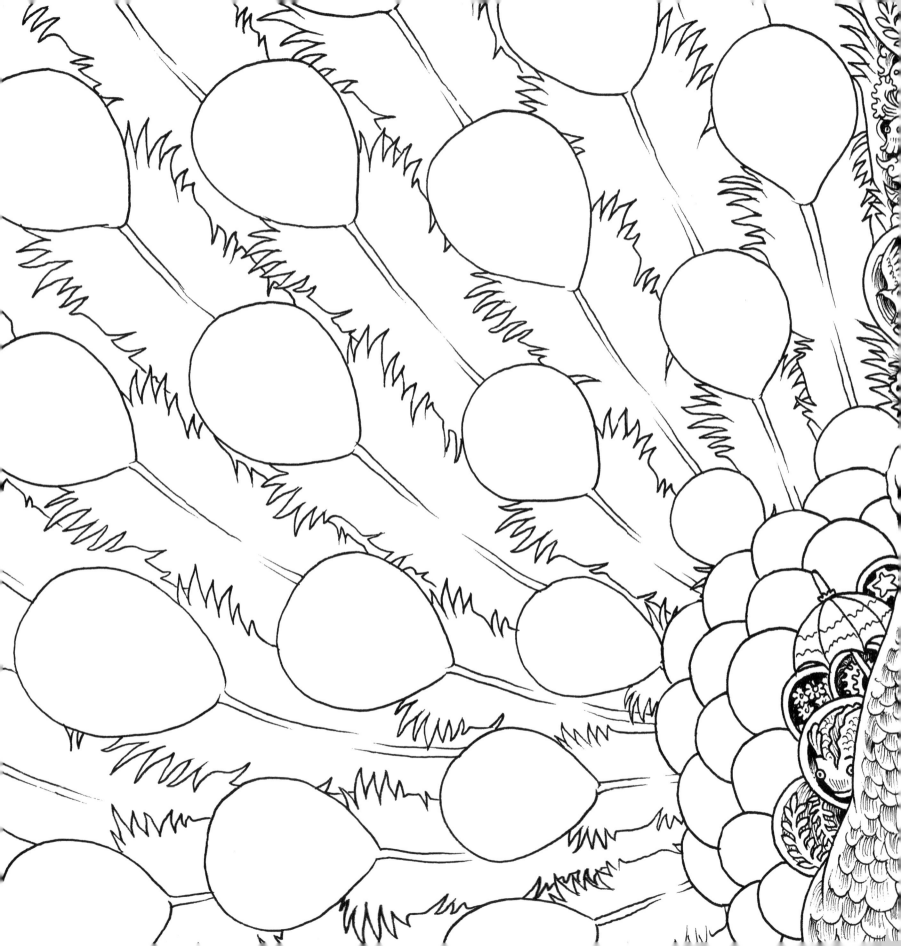

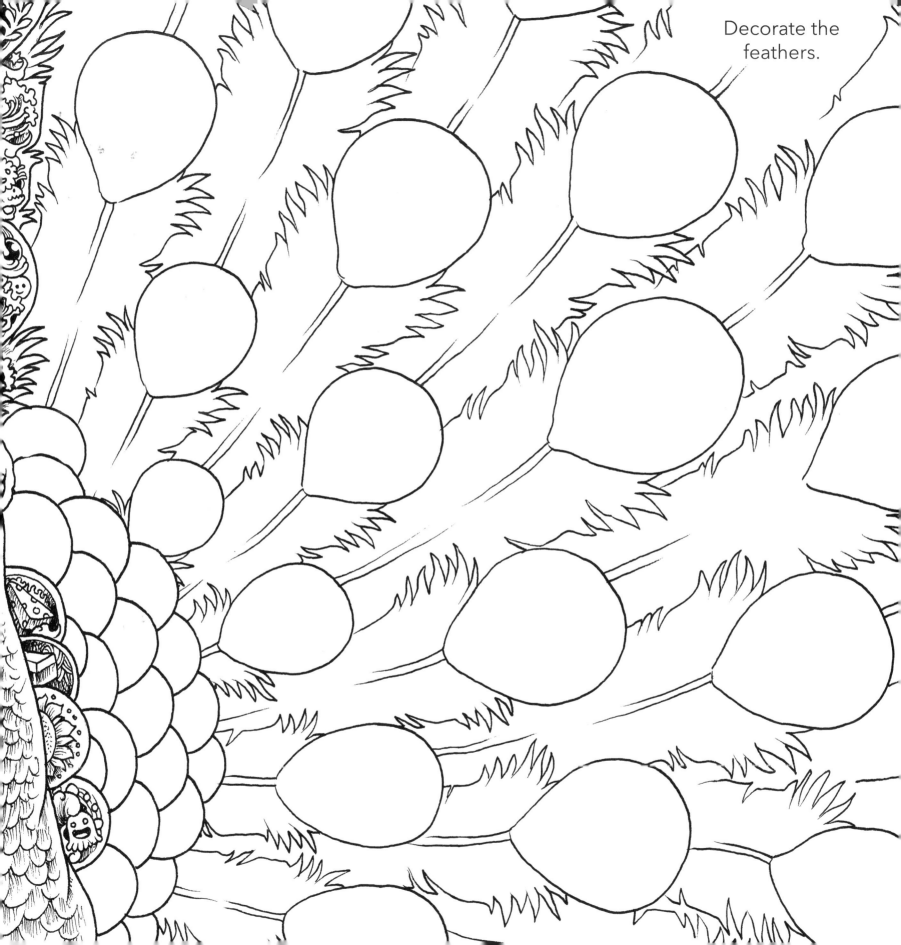

Decorate the feathers.

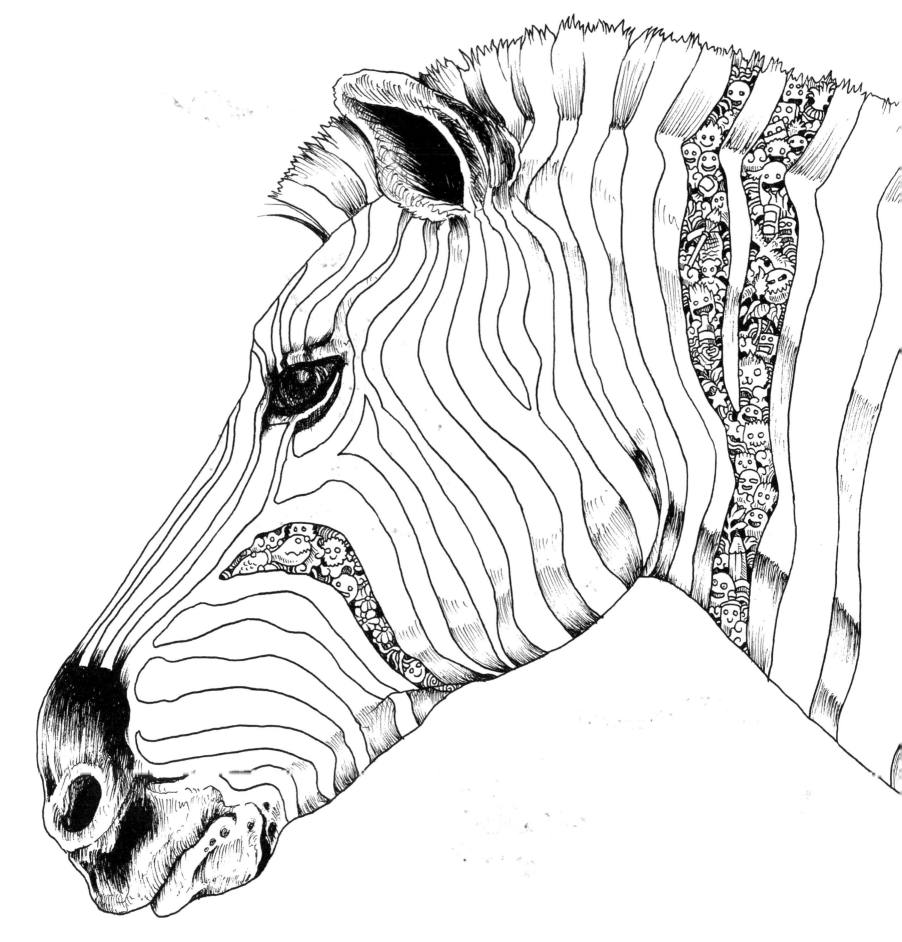

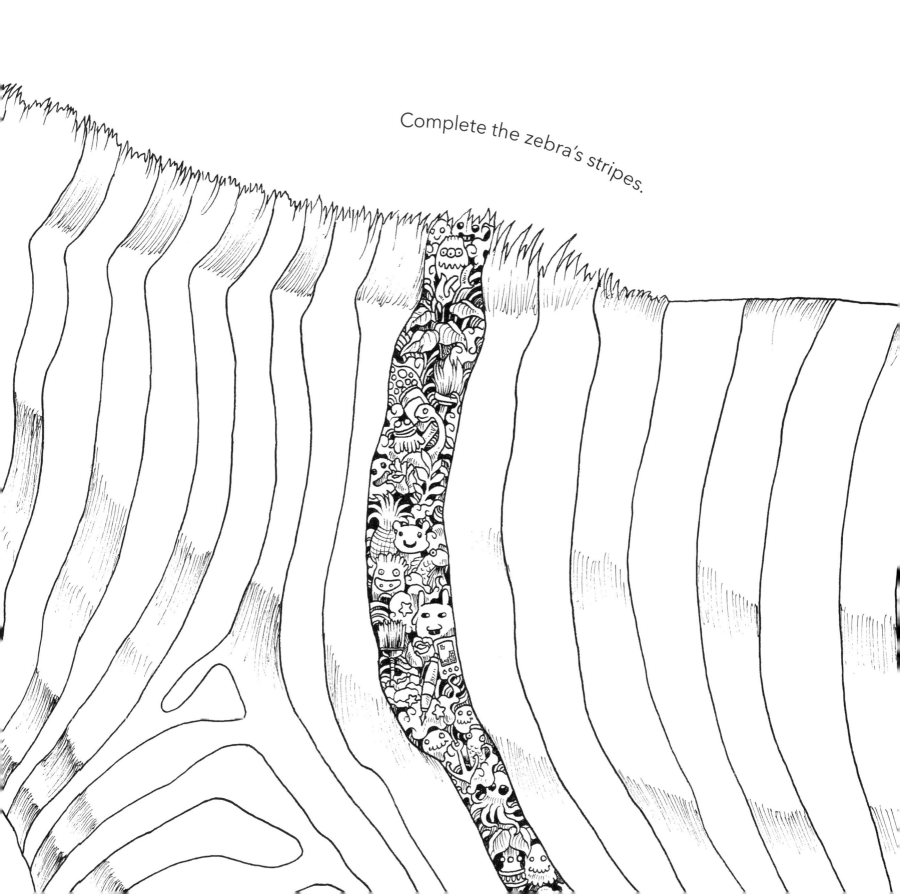

Complete the zebra's stripes.

Complete the
lion's mane.

Fill the page with bats.

Decorate the turtles' shells.

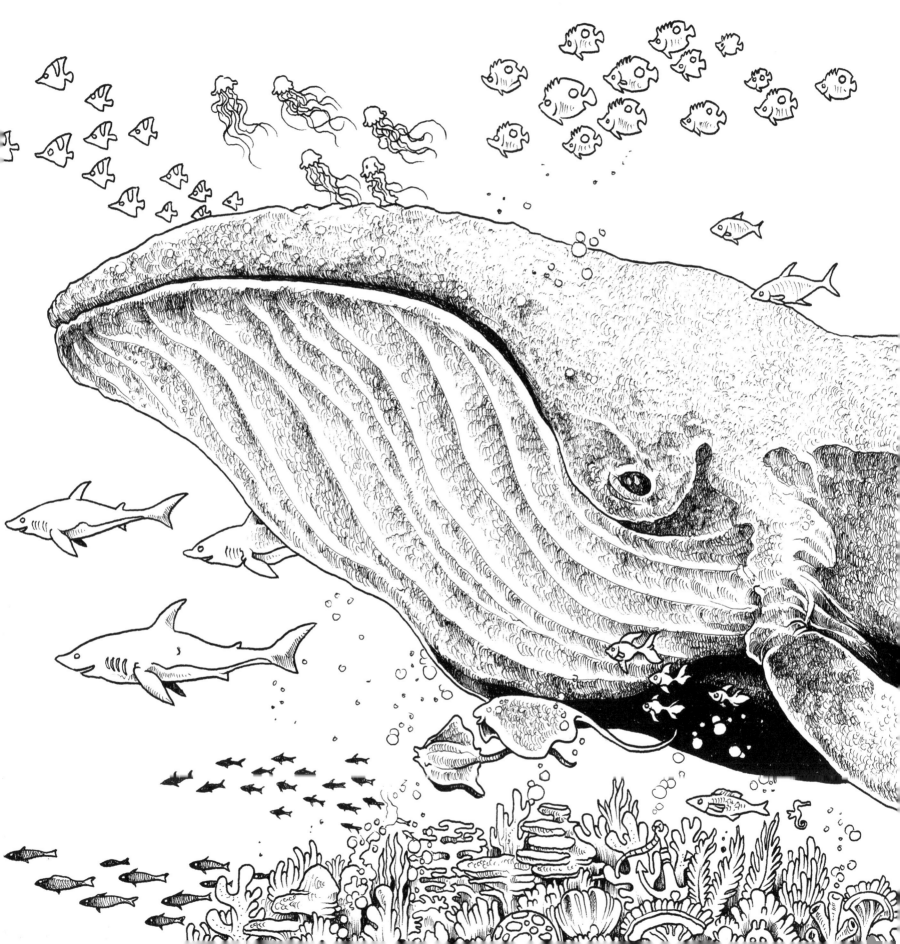

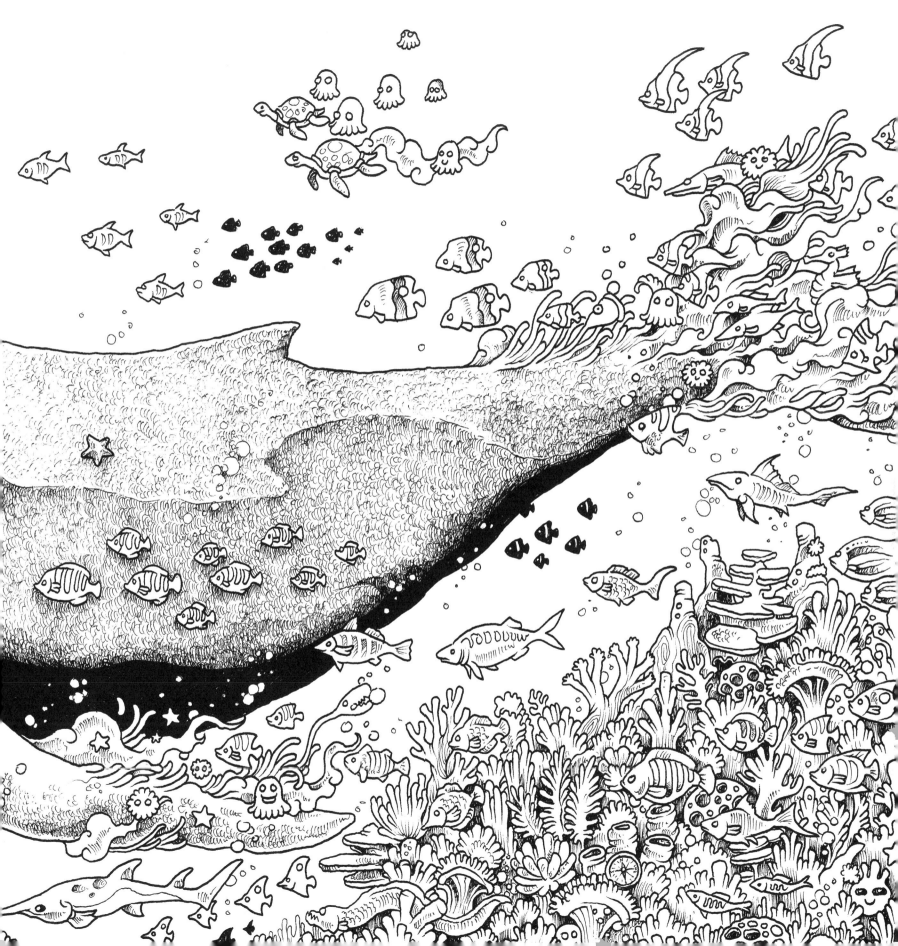

Embellish the elephant with
detailed patterns.

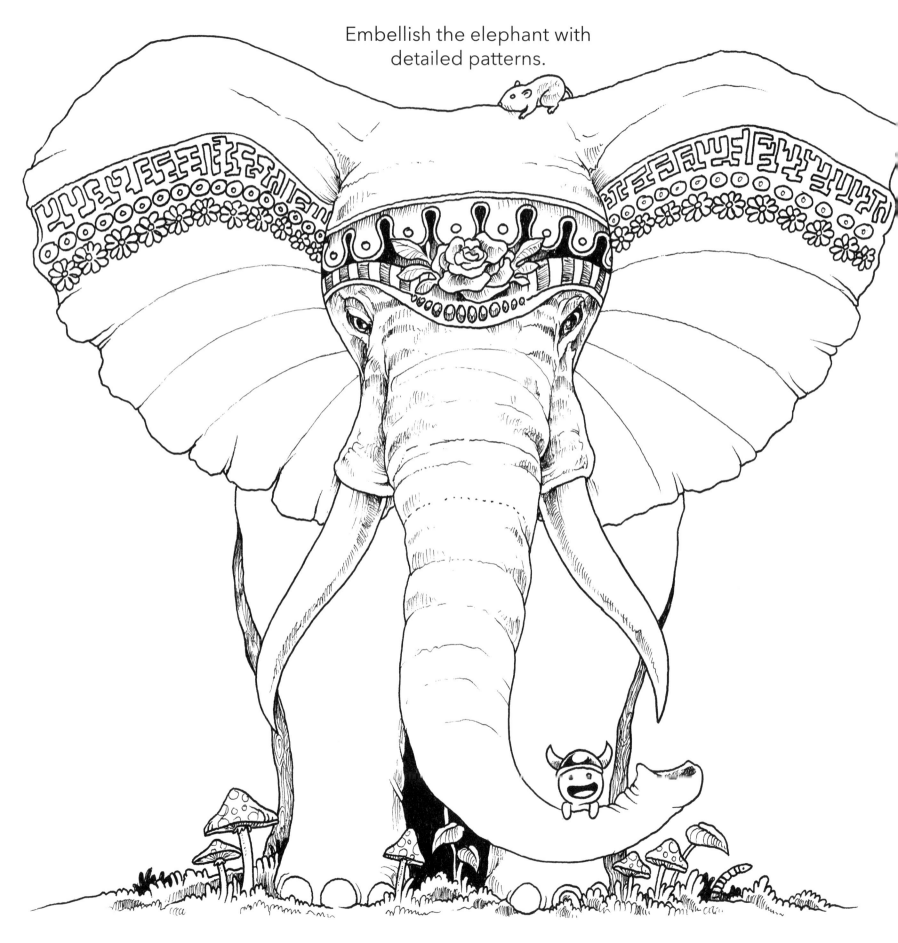

Doodle more crows.

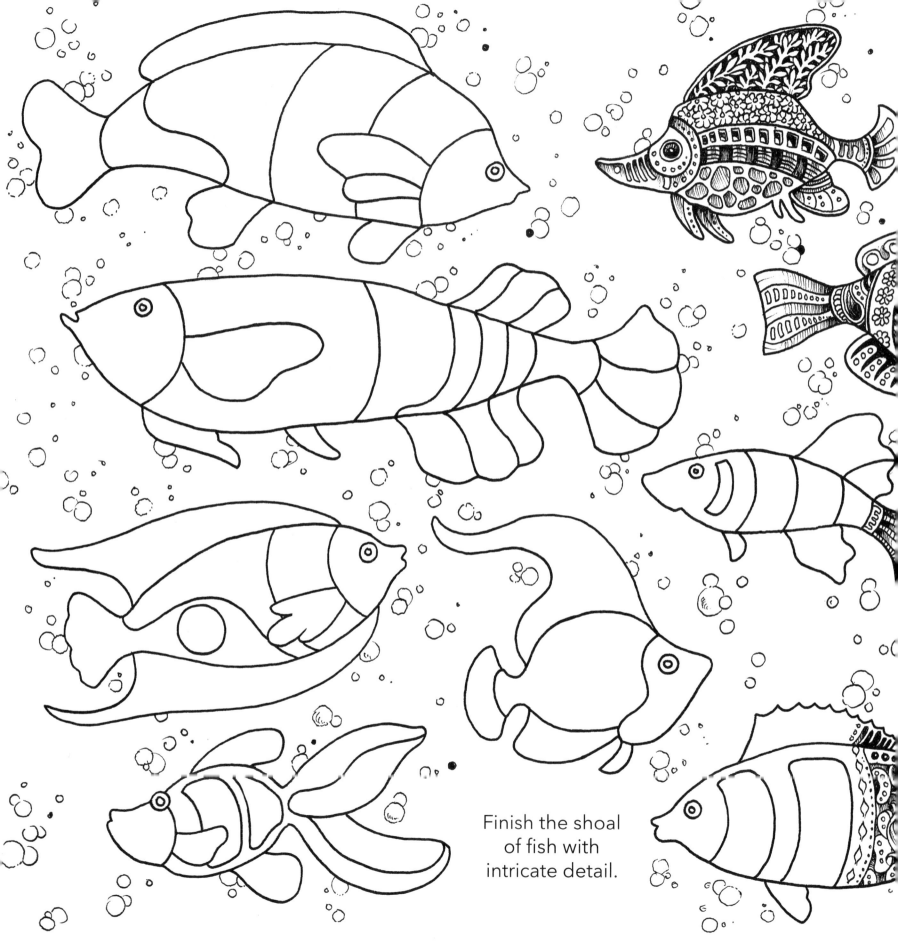

Finish the shoal
of fish with
intricate detail.

Draw more jellyfish to fill the page.

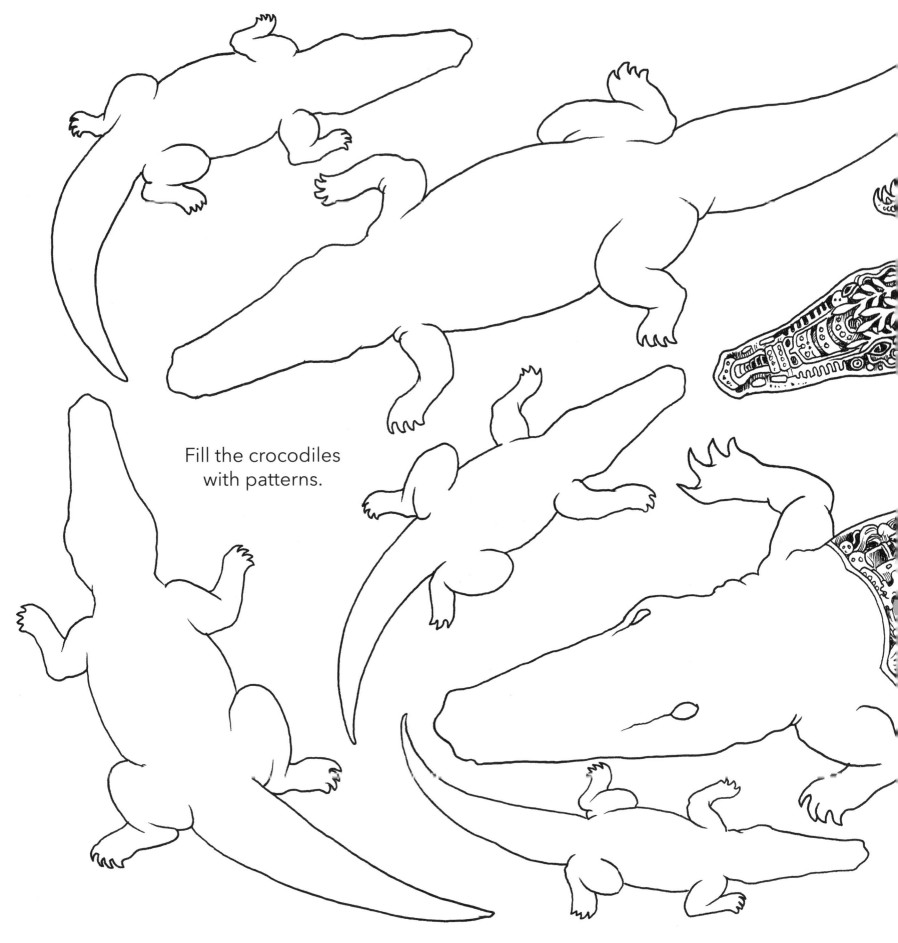

Fill the crocodiles
with patterns.

Complete this
pod of orcas.

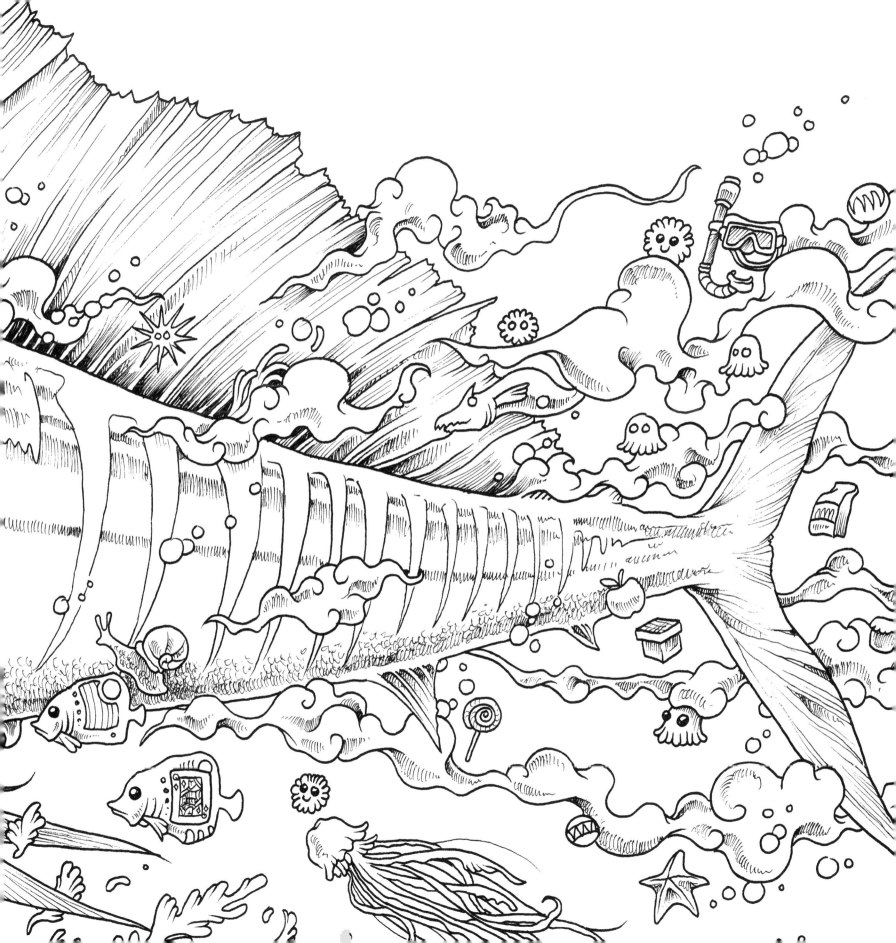

Draw more bees bumbling towards the flowers.

Can you find these items, artefacts and creatures in the book?

When you have discovered them, colour in the objects on the next few pages.

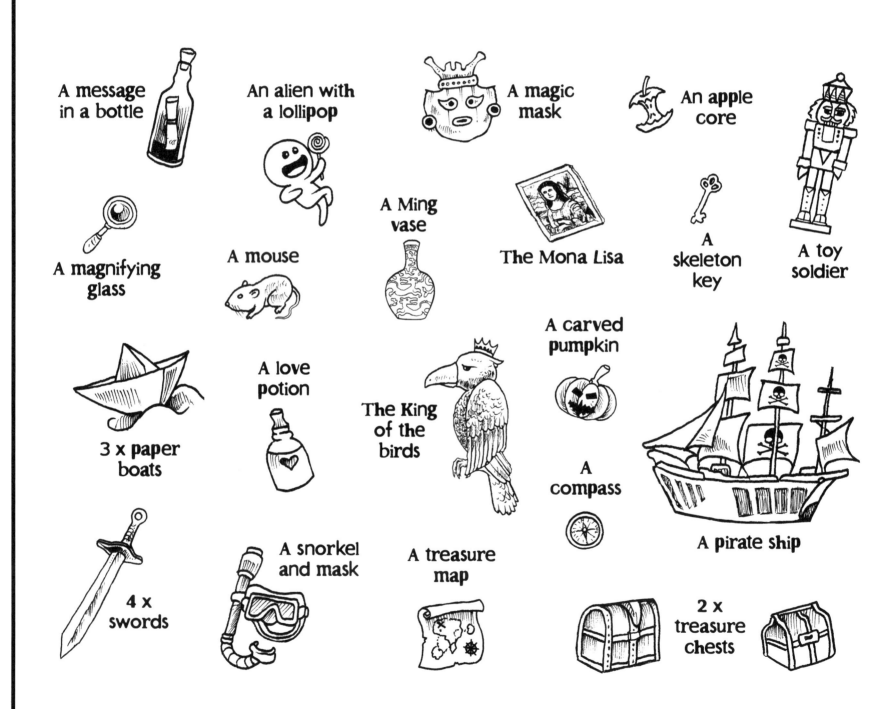

A message in a bottle

An alien with a lollipop

A magic mask

An apple core

A magnifying glass

A mouse

A Ming vase

The Mona Lisa

A skeleton key

A toy soldier

3 x paper boats

A love potion

The King of the birds

A carved pumpkin

A compass

A pirate ship

4 x swords

A snorkel and mask

A treasure map

2 x treasure chests

An alien
vampire

7 x
basketballs

An animal
playing with
this toy car

A running
shoe

A retro
TV

The King of
the reptiles

A goldfish
in a bowl

A hang-gliding
alien

A violin

A ping-pong
bat

A pair of
sunglasses

Croc-dog

A fountain
pen

This doll

4 x Rubik's
Cubes

These
throwing
darts

A fossil

An
hourglass

A love
letter

A sock

A dice

A spell
book

A postage
stamp

Alien Elvis

An old
boot

5 x open
umbrellas

This big
spider

A missile

2 x surfing aliens

A sparkly bracelet

The King of the mammals

A scroll

A football

A scary doll

A watch on an animal's wrist

A drum with sticks

This grumpy caterpillar

This goblin

An alien witch

The Ace of Diamonds

The Ace of Spades

The Ace of Clubs

The Ace of Hearts

The King of Diamonds

The King of Clubs

The King of Spades

The King of Hearts

A yo-yo

A laptop

The Queen of Diamonds

The Queen of Spades

The Queen of Clubs

The Queen of Hearts

The Joker in the pack

A dinosaur egg

All the
Answers

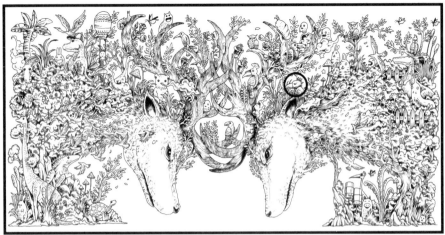

The King of the birds

A surfing alien

The Ace of Diamonds, a laptop and a basketball

A magic mask, a Rubik's Cube and a sword

A treasure map

The Ace of Hearts, a running shoe and a basketball

A carved pumpkin, a spell book and a Rubik's Cube

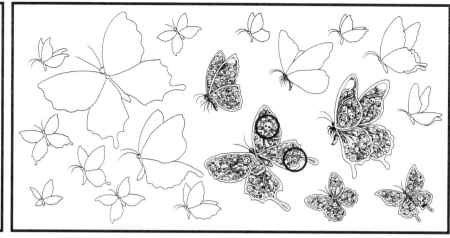

Alien Elvis and a basketball

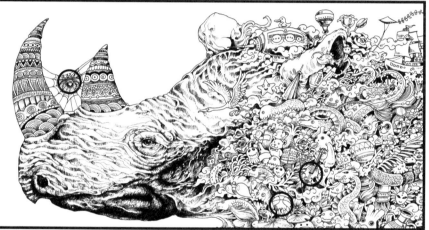

A big spider, a basketball and a violin

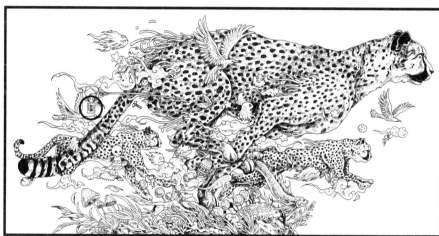

The Joker in the pack

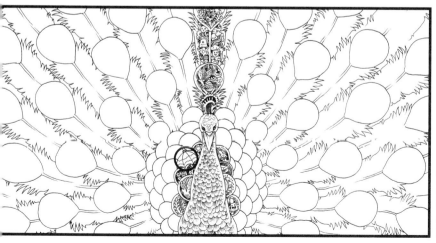

An open umbrella

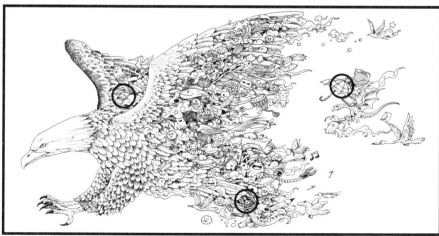

The Mona Lisa, an open umbrella and a basketball

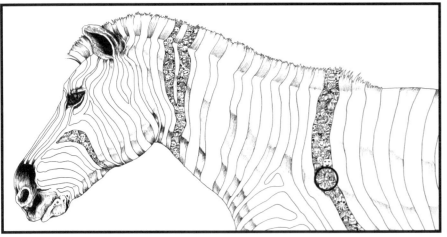

A fountain pen

An alien with a lollipop

A postage stamp, a paper boat and an apple core

An hourglass and an alien vampire

A Rubik's Cube and an alien witch

A fossil and a magnifying glass

The Ace of Spades, a football, a love letter
and a watch on an animal's wrist

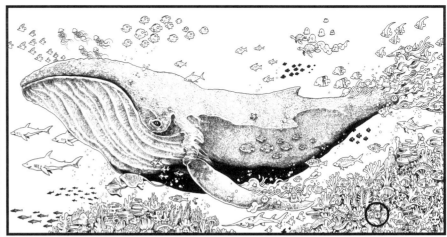

A compass

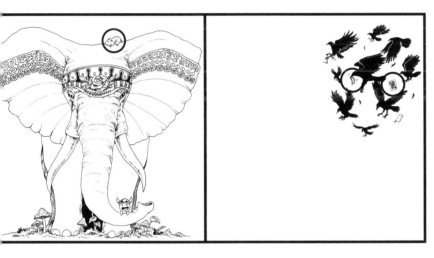

A mouse, the King of Clubs and a sparkly bracelet

The Ace of Clubs, an open umbrella and a Ming vase

An old boot

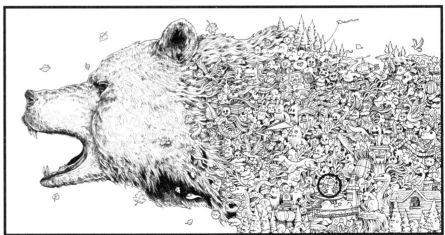

A surfing alien

A ping-pong bat, a sword and a message in a bottle

A treasure chest

A doll, a paper boat, a sock and a skeleton key

A dinosaur egg, a love potion,
a goblin and a scary doll

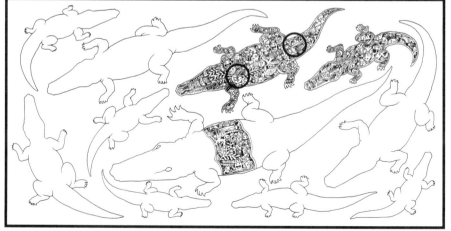

A goldfish in a bowl and a sword

The King of the mammals, an open umbrella,
a scroll, a basketball and a sword

The King of Hearts, a grumpy
caterpillar and a missile

The Queen of Hearts, the throwing
darts and a hang-gliding alien

A paper boat and a pair of sunglasses

The King of Spades, a yo-yo and a basketball

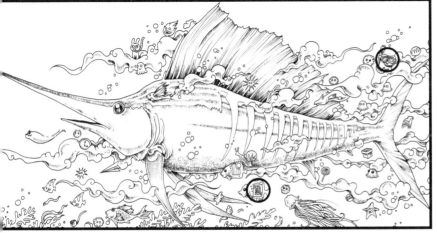

The Queen of Diamonds and a snorkel and mask

The Queen of Clubs, a Rubik's Cube,
a toy soldier and a drum with sticks

The King of Diamonds and a dice

The Queen of Spades and a pirate ship

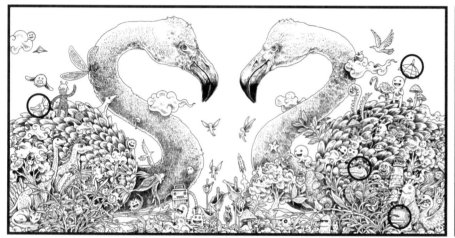

The King of the reptiles, Croc-dog,
a retro TV and an open umbrella

An animal playing with a toy
car and a treasure chest

The end

Share your creations:
#animorphia